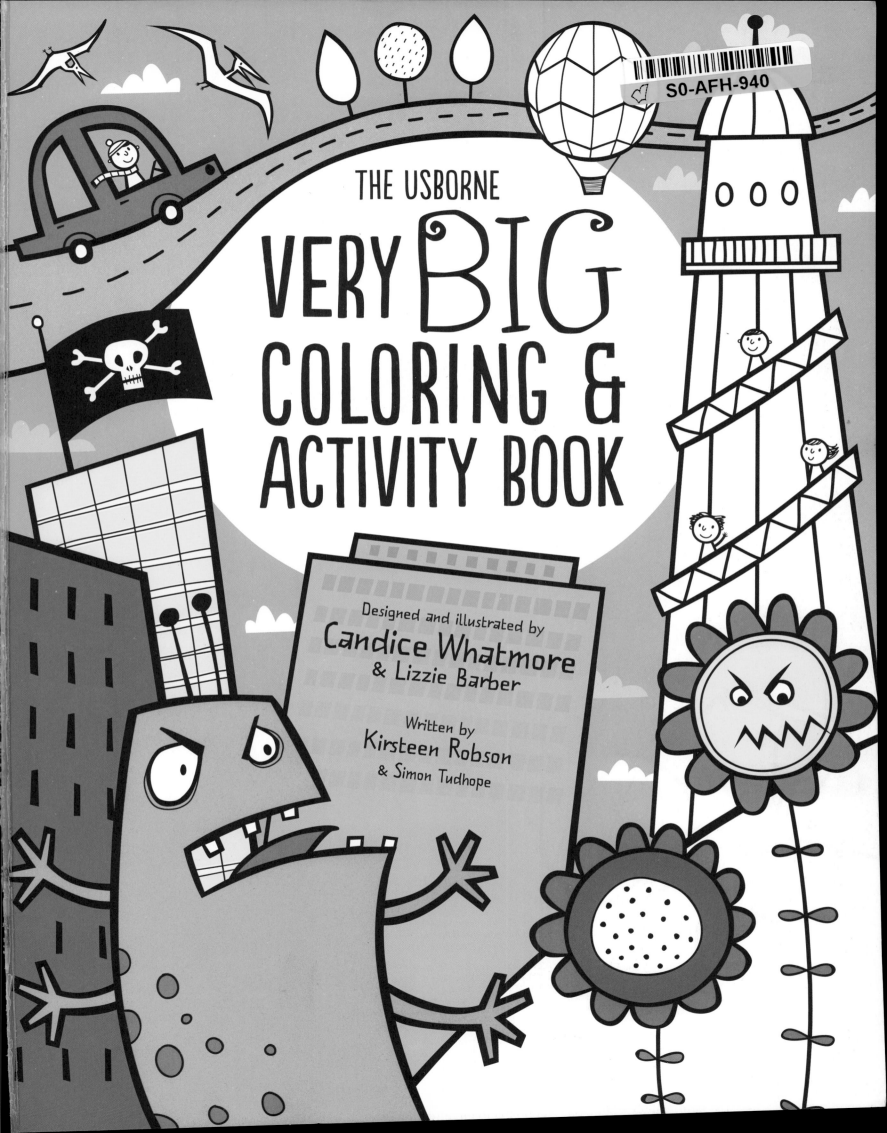

THE USBORNE

VERY BIG COLORING & ACTIVITY BOOK

Designed and illustrated by
Candice Whatmore
& Lizzie Barber

Written by
Kirsteen Robson
& Simon Tudhope

With thanks to Keith Furnival
Expert consultants: Tony Pawlyn (Pirates), Dr. Darren Naish (Dinosaurs),
Dr. Abigail Wheatley (Knights & Castles)

First published in 2013 by Usborne Publishing Ltd. 83–85 Saffron Hill, London EC1N 8RT, England.
Copyright ©2013, 2012, 2011, 2010, 2009 Usborne Publishing Ltd. The name Usborne and the
devices ♀ ⊕ are Trade Marks of Usborne Publishing Ltd.
First Printed in America in 2014. AE

CONTENTS

Coloring hints and tips

You could use felt-tip pens or colored pencils to color in the pictures. Felt-tip pens will give you strong colors, while pencils will have a softer effect.

You can draw patterns within some of the shapes. For example, these pictures are decorated with waves and wiggles...

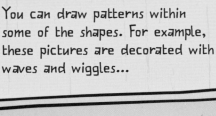

...spots and dots...

You could finish these pictures to practice coloring.

...zigzags and stripes.

Fill in larger areas such as this shield with lots of lines going in the same direction.

It's a good idea to lay your book on a flat surface while you are coloring, or slip a piece of cardboard under the page you are filling in, to make a firm surface.

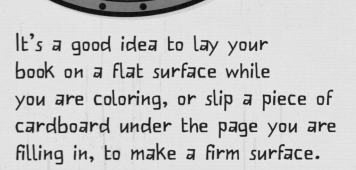

If you'd like to cut out your picture, you can cut along this dotted line.

VACATION

Decorate the fish

Add stripes, spots and squiggles to these fish, to make them feel at home among the bright corals and weeds in their tropical lagoon.

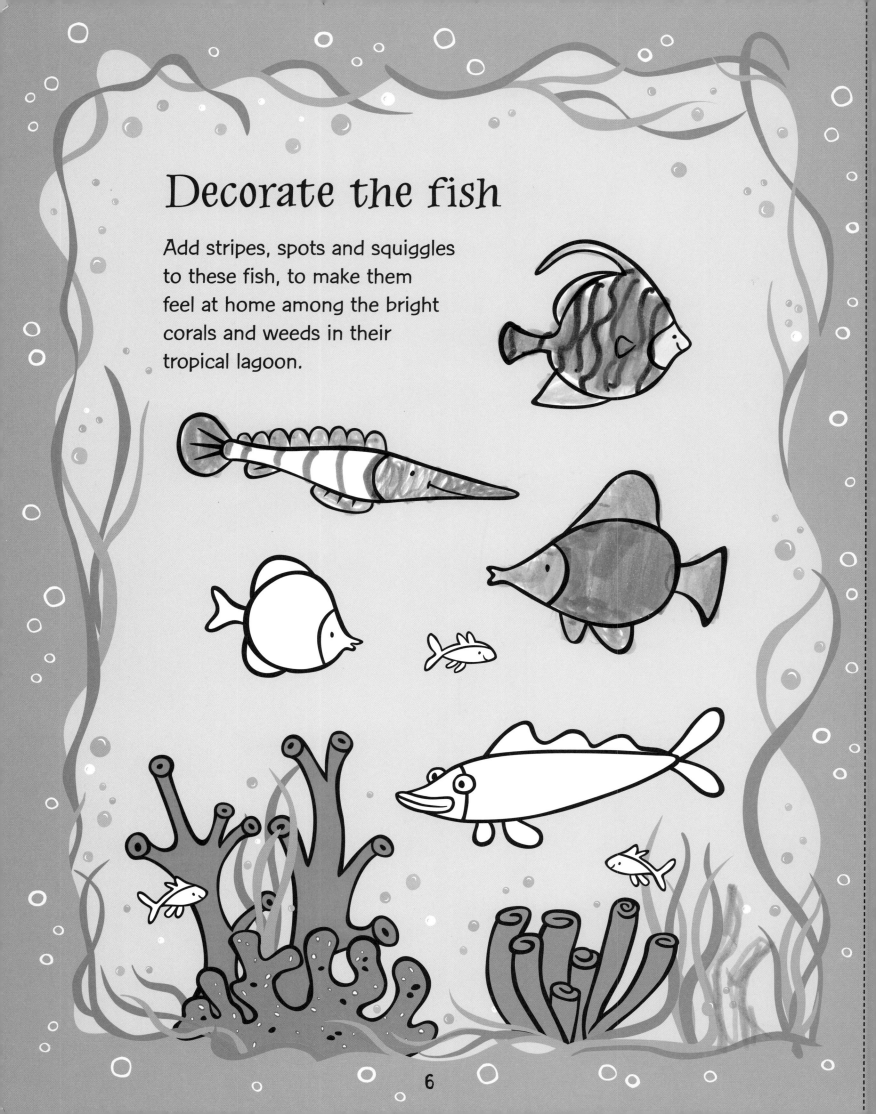

Build a sandcastle

Draw over the dotted lines to make sand towers and turrets. Decorate your castle with shells, pebbles and seaweed.

8

Fill in the passports

Add names and details to these passports, then design some stamps for exciting places you'd love to visit.

PASSPORT

NAME ....

DATE OF BIRTH ....

NATIONALITY ....

PLACES I'D LIKE TO VISIT

Draw your face here.

PASSPORT

NAME ....

DATE OF BIRTH ....

NATIONALITY ....

Going camping

Draw over the dotted lines to find out what's hanging from this handy clothesline. Then add some camping gear of your own.

Whip up a sundae

Create a mouthwatering ice cream sundae in each glass. Invent your own treat in one, and use the customer's order to fill the other.

2 scoops vanilla ice cream
fudge pieces
1 scoop chocolate ice cream
whipped cream
wafer rolls
sugar sprinkles

Order 36

Specials

$2

$3

Toppings

- Raspberry sauce
- Strawberry sauce
- Chocolate sauce
- Fudge sauce
- Fresh fruits
- Marshmallows
- Chocolate chips
- Fudge pieces
- Candy sprinkles
- Wafer fans

Picnic in the park

Draw your favorite foods on the plate and fill the glass with something delicious to make a perfect picnic.

Rig the boats

Draw over the dotted lines to give these bobbing boats sails and flags. Then decorate them any way you like.

Fairground fun

Give these prancing carousel ponies striped poles, and cover their bodies with pretty patterns.

Balloon festival

The sky is dotted with drifting hot-air balloons. Decorate these any way you like.

On safari

Draw over the dotted lines to finish the vacation snapshots below. Then draw the animal you'd most like to see on a wildlife safari.

Draw your photo here.

Make a tide pool

Draw over the dotted lines to discover what's sheltering in the tide pool. Then bring the pool to life by adding some creatures of your own.

Pack your suitcase

Write a list of things you'd like to take away with you on vacation. Remember to include books and toys too. If you could only take one item with you, what would you choose?

Things to pack . . .

Chloë Smith
15 White Oak Drive
Anyville, Oklahoma
USA

Traffic trouble

Transform these shapes into cars
by adding wheels and passengers.

Airport
2 miles

Draw pictures on these
delivery trucks to show
what they're carrying.

Ski school

Give these sporty penguins skis and ski poles to help them slalom down the slippery ski-run. Wheee!

Seaside town

Turn these buildings into bright and cheery seaside stores by giving them names and filling their windows with things to sell.

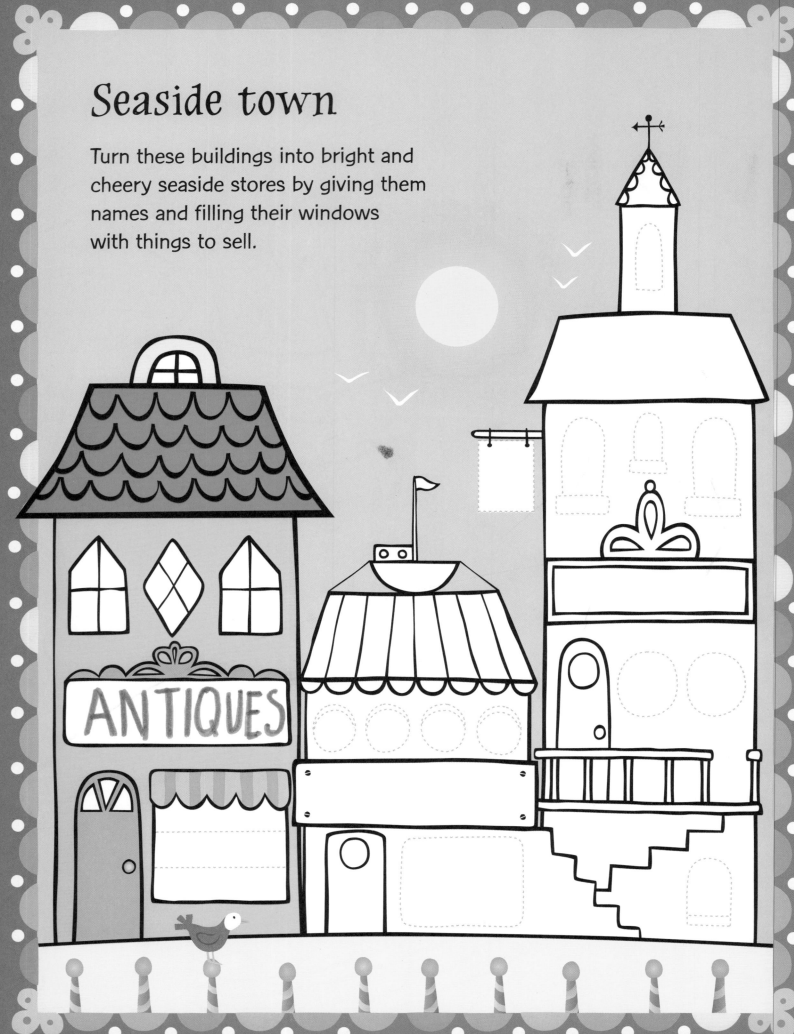

ANTIQUES

Bright sails

See how many patterns and colors you can get into this picture.
Try spots and stars on the sails, and fill the sea with wiggly waves.

Who's who in a pirate crew

Pirates were ruthless robbers who roamed the salty seas in search of ships or vulnerable seaside villages to steal from. Far from being a lazy, lawless lot, pirates had to work as a disciplined team, and most men had particular jobs to do to keep the vessel shipshape and the crew alive.

Here are descriptions of a few important characters on board a pirate ship. Can you match them to the correct pictures?

1. The captain was voted into the job by his men. He was expected to be a skilled sailor and a bold leader in battle.

2. The quartermaster was second in command. He shared out food, gunpowder, loot, work and punishment.

3. The ship's carpenter was responsible for mending the ship – filling in the holes and keeping it seaworthy.

A

B

C

D

E

F

4. Rats and mice ran riot on ships, so a canny crew often carried a cat to keep these rodent rascals under control.

5. The cabin boy was learning the pirate trade. He often ran errands for the captain, and laid out his clothes.

6. Fortunate crews had a surgeon to treat their injuries. Less lucky shipmates had to make do with anyone who could brandish a blade.

The Jolly Roger

No pirate ship was complete without a "Jolly Roger" – a fearsome flag displaying a doom-laden design that would strike terror into the heart of anyone who saw it. A skull and crossbones was a popular emblem, but anything would do as long as its message was clear and threatening.

Create your own bloodcurdling Jolly Roger design.

These pictures show some popular alternatives to the traditional skull-and-crossbones emblem.

  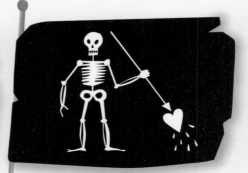

Pirate provisions

Before setting sail, pirates needed to stock up on supplies. The list below includes some of the things they would need to take with them to sea. (The pictures on the right include some more lighthearted suggestions.)

See if you can find the words below in the grid. They may be written in any direction. Starting at the top, read the unused letters to spell the first lines of a pirate song from a famous pirate story.

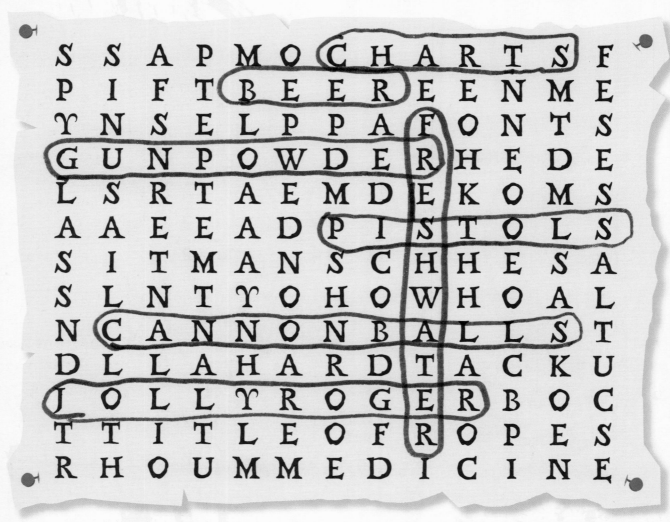

```
S S A P M O C H A R T S F
P I F T B E E R E E N M E
Y N S E L P P A F O N T S
G U N P O W D E R H E D E
L S R T A E M D E K O M S
A A E E A D P I S T O L S
S I T M A N S C H H E S A
S L N T Y O H O W H O A L
N C A N N O N B A L L S T
D L L A H A R D T A C K U
J O L L Y R O G E R B O C
T T I T L E O F R O P E S
R H O U M M E D I C I N E
```

APPLES • BEER • CANNONBALLS • CHARTS • COMPASS • CUTLASSES
FRESH WATER • GUNPOWDER • HARD TACK • JOLLY ROGER • MEDICINE
OIL LANTERNS • PISTOLS • ROPES • SAILCLOTH • SMOKED MEAT • SPY GLASS

Mealtime misery

It was incredibly difficult to keep food fresh for long during a voyage, so mealtimes often caused pirates more dread than delight. Here you can find out about some of the foods a pirate might find on his plate.

Show how many eggs Clucky has laid this week.

At the start of a voyage pirates ate fresh meat, cheese, vegetables and eggs. Livestock such as hens and cows lived on board for as long as they could be fed, then they were eaten.

Doodle in the basket to show what the pirates have caught in their nets.

Pirates might catch fresh fish or turtles at sea to add variety to their diet.

Draw another barrel of salted meat.

SALT PORK

Meat could be preserved by salting or smoking it and sealing it in barrels. Meat preserved in this way was tough and chewy.

What's he thinking?

In 1670, the starving pirate crew of Sir Henry Morgan sliced up their leather satchels, roasted them and ate them.

Add more weevils to the hard tack.

Hard tack - dry bread made of flour and water. Pirates often ate it in the dark so they couldn't see the weevils that had infested them.

Fill in the flasks to show what this pirate is drinking today.

Water soon went stale in its dusty barrels, so pirates often drank beer or rum. If this ran out, they might have to drink salty seawater or even their own urine.

Rules and punishments

Although pirates lived outside the law of the land, they had their own strict code of conduct. There were unpleasant punishments for anyone found flouting the rules.

Popular pirate punishments included:
• being tied to a mast and whipped with a frayed rope called a cat-o'-nine-tails
• being towed behind the boat in the freezing water for a day or two
• being marooned (left alone on a desert island)

If you were a pirate captain, what rules would you add to the list (if your crew agreed) and what would be the punishment for breaking them?

Pirate rules

1. Equal vote for all
2. No stealing from shipmates
3. No gambling on board
4. Lights out at 8 o'clock
5. Keep your weapons clean
6. No women on board
7. No deserting – stick together
8. No fighting shipmates at sea
9. Treasure shared fairly according to rank
10. Musicians have Sundays off

Rule	Punishment

After eight

Lights out was at 8 o'clock sharp. While the captain curled up in a comfortable bed in his private cabin, the rest of the crew hauled themselves into grubby hammocks in the belly of the ship. There in the stuffy darkness, amid hissing cockroaches and the scratching of scrounging rats, they were rocked to sleep by the rhythm of the restless waves.

Show whether this slumbering sailor is snarling or smiling, and draw his dream.

48

Ship ahoy!

On spying a merchant ship crossing their path, pirates had two choices. They could take down their Jolly Roger and hoist a normal flag instead to let the other ship think it was safe to get close (until it was too late). Or they could make themselves look as menacing and merciless as possible to fill their enemies with tummy-trembling terror.

If the pirates had already captured a few ships, they might raise a pirate flag on each of them to look like a whole fleet of pirate vessels. Add more flags, masts and sails to the boats below.

Moonlight marauders

Thinking the merchant sailors are sweetly slumbering, these bold buccaneers have swarmed aboard with bloodcurdling bellows. But a swift and sinister hiss of steel tells them that their opponents have been waiting watchfully for them, and a bloody battle begins...

Read about some of the weapons that might be used in a raid.

Daggers were handy knives for hiding in pockets to whip out and surprise enemies.

Cutlasses were short, sharp slashing swords, often with a cupped or basket-shaped hand guard.

Spiked iron caltrops (or crowsfeet) were scattered on deck, ready to pierce the (often bare) feet of unsuspecting sailors.

Pistols were fine for flooring foes from afar, but they were awkward to aim accurately on choppy seas. (Damp gunpowder didn't fire well either, and it took ages to reload them.)

Grappling hooks could be thrown into the rigging, or over the side of another ship, to drag it close enough to jump aboard.

Grenadoes were gunpowder-filled throwing balls of iron or wood that exploded when the fuse was lit.

Sometimes pirates added tar and rags to the grenado mixture, creating choking clouds of black smoke to cause confusion.

Myths and mistakes

Pirates have captured the imagination of so many storytellers and movie-makers that all kinds of fables are now thought of as facts. For instance, some pirates may have lost a leg or an eye, but a ship couldn't sail without plenty of able-bodied crewmen. And few real pirates would bother to make their prisoners walk the plank – they'd just push them overboard.

How to draw a storybook pirate captain

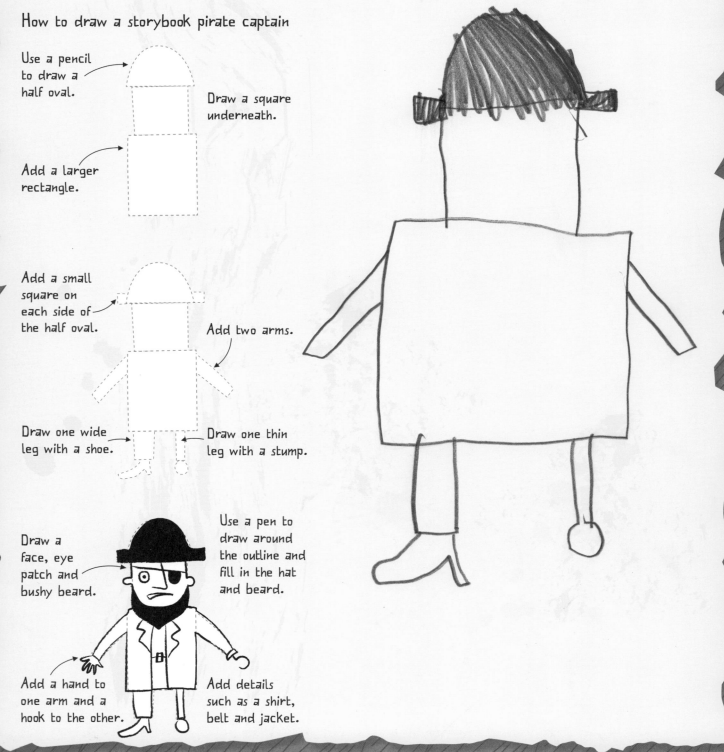

Use a pencil to draw a half oval.

Draw a square underneath.

Add a larger rectangle.

Add a small square on each side of the half oval.

Add two arms.

Draw one wide leg with a shoe.

Draw one thin leg with a stump.

Draw a face, eye patch and bushy beard.

Use a pen to draw around the outline and fill in the hat and beard.

Add a hand to one arm and a hook to the other.

Add details such as a shirt, belt and jacket.

Pirate pastimes

Aside from surviving sea battles and storms, much of a pirate's time was spent keeping the ship seaworthy – patching sails, splicing (joining) ropes and making sure the woodwork was watertight. Once their jobs were done, nothing could beat singing a few swinging sea shanties to keep boredom at bay, or sneaking a few forbidden games of cards or dice.

Finish the pirate faces.

The truth about treasure

After a successful skirmish, a lucky looter might find a stash of coins or jewels, but fresh food and medicine were rich rewards too. People could also be priceless prizes – think how popular a pirate would be with his wounded shipmates if he brought a super-skilled surgeon back on board.

When it came to dividing the booty, pirates were usually fair fellows and took (more or less) equal shares. Use the clues below to find out who took each piece of treasure from their latest conquest.

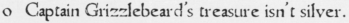

- o Captain Grizzlebeard's treasure isn't silver.

- o Mumbles McGraw can't use his treasure at the table.

- o The ugliest pirate has the most delicate and decorative prize.

Spanish gold doubloons – each one was worth about a week's wages for an ordinary pirate.

Silverware

Necklaces

Pieces of eight were silver coins made in Spain.

Captain Grizzlebeard   Mumbles McGraw   Scurvy Joe Jones   Scarface Jake

Treasure map

In real life, pirates would usually trade or gamble with their share of a treasure haul, or take it home. If they *did* decide to hide it for safekeeping, a map was probably the worst way to keep their secret safe. But this has not stopped treasure maps from playing an important part in many pirate tales.

These instructions describe two routes to some buried treasure. Captain Crossbones took the first route and Captain Cutthroat followed the second. Who reached the treasure first?

From the pointed pair on the island of mud, head west to the isle of fiery rock. Sail south to the place where the dolphins dive then travel eastward until a monster blocks thy path. Steer to the south then drop anchor and trek to the mountains of mist and shadow. Wend thy way between the three and the one then seek the swirling plain of shifting sands. Head southwest and dig under the lonely pine tree for thy prize.

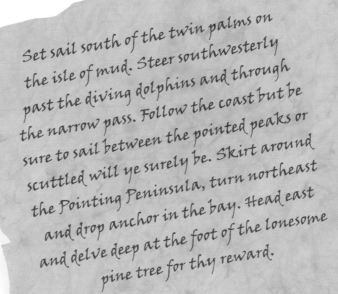

Set sail south of the twin palms on the isle of mud. Steer southwesterly past the diving dolphins and through the narrow pass. Follow the coast but be sure to sail between the pointed peaks or scuttled will ye surely be. Skirt around the Pointing Peninsula, turn northeast and drop anchor in the bay. Head east and delve deep at the foot of the lonesome pine tree for thy reward.

Offshore dangers

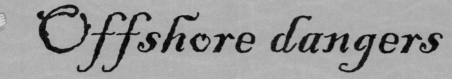

Out at sea, wild winds could whip the waters into a frenzy, sinking the sturdiest of ships. Or smothering fogs could force ships to sail blind until they were lost beyond hope or ruined on the razor-toothed rocks. And as if these terrors weren't enough, seafarers shared superstitious tales of vast sea monsters with thrashing tentacles that brought doom and destruction.

Help the ship to avoid the obstacles and navigate its way safely to the sandy island.

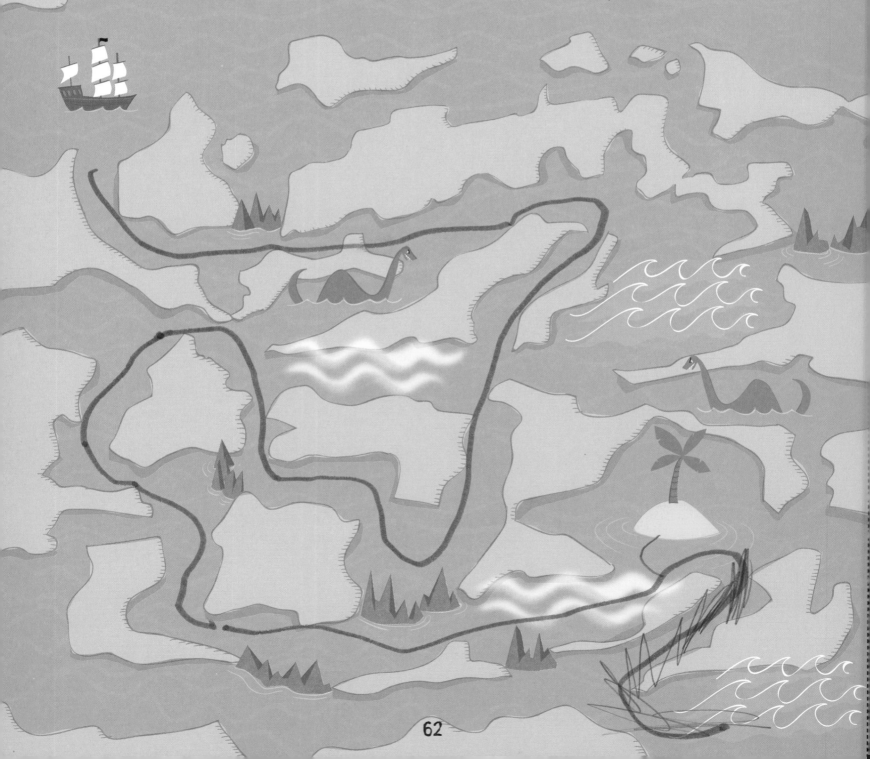

The perils of piracy

Pirates' lives were often short. Shipwreck, starvation or sickness sent many sailors straight to Davy Jones' Locker (that's pirate-speak for the seabed.) Cannon fire or combat ended plenty of promising pirate careers while some sea dogs were captured by the navy and hanged for their crimes. Only the luckiest old salts survived to enjoy their pirated plunder into retirement.

You could use this space to write your own tale of pirate adventure.

"Ahoy there!" shouted Captain . . . .

"Where can I find . . . .

. . . .

. . . .

. . . .

. . . .

. . . .

. . . .

. . . .

The end

Rogues' Gallery

Some pirates became famous as tales of their treachery spread far and wide. Over time, their dreadful deeds inspired writers to spin stories about pirate characters of their own. On the opposite page you can find out more about a few of the most famous fiends of fact and fiction.

Why not draw your own pirate character, and give him a name?

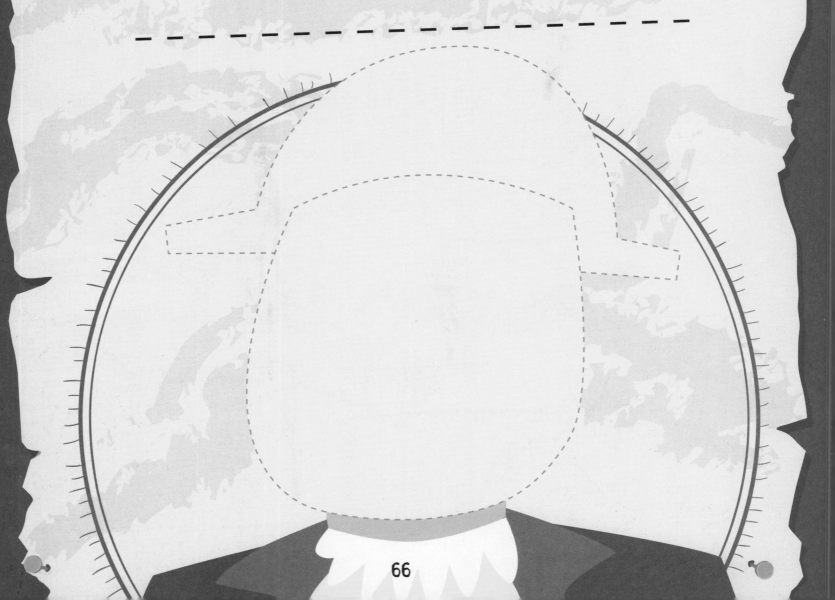

WANTED!
FOR PIRACY AND LOOTING

LONG JOHN SILVER

Long John Silver was a fictional pirate from the book 'Treasure Island' by Robert Louis Stevenson. Silver's left leg had been cut off at the hip after a sea battle, but he hopped around very nimbly using a crutch. He had a parrot companion named Captain Flint who sat on his shoulder. In the book Silver and his shipmates trick their way onto an expedition in search of buried treasure.

Henry Morgan

Henry Morgan was a privateer which meant he had permission from the government to raid foreign ships. He became one of the richest pirates ever.

Black Bart

Nicknamed Black Bart, Bartholomew Roberts was a daredevil pirate famous for attacking ships that had more cannons than his. Unusually for a pirate, he was well known for preferring a tankard of tea to a tot of rum. He gained the reputation for being invincible — until his death four years into his pirate career.

BLACKBEARD

Blackbeard's real (but less terrifying) name was Edward Teach. To boost his already alarming image, he sometimes tucked burning ropes under his hat, cloaking himself in clouds of smoke.

Captain Hook

Captain James Hook is a character in J.M. Barrie's book 'Peter Pan.' The pirate's name refers to the large metal hook he wore in place of his right hand, which Peter Pan had cut off and fed to a crocodile. The croc liked the taste so much it followed Hook around, hoping to finish its meal.

MARY READ AND ANN BONNY

Women were strictly forbidden on pirate ships, so female pirates were rare. Mary Read and Ann Bonny disguised themselves as men and joined the pirate crew of a captain named Calico Jack. They fought even more fiercely than their male shipmates.

Pirate answers

Page 38

1.B   2.F   3.A   4.E   5.D   6.C

Page 42

```
S  S  A  P  M  O  C  H  A  R  T  S  F
P  I  F  T  B  E  E  R  E  E  N  M  E
Y  N  S  E  L  P  P  A  F  O  N  T  S
G  U  N  P  O  W  D  E  R  H  E  D  E
L  S  R  T  A  E  M  D  E  K  O  M  S
A  A  E  E  A  D  P  I  S  T  O  L  S
S  I  T  M  A  N  S  C  H  H  E  S  A
S  L  N  T  Y  O  H  O  W  H  O  A  L
N  C  A  N  N  O  N  B  A  L  L  S  T
D  L  L  A  H  A  R  D  T  A  C  K  U
J  O  L  L  Y  R  O  G  E  R  B  O  C
T  T  I  T  L  E  O  F  R  O  P  E  S
R  H  O  U  M  M  E  D  I  C  I  N  E
```

FIFTEEN MEN ON THE DEAD MAN'S CHEST
– YO-HO-HO, AND A BOTTLE OF RUM!

Page 58

Captain Grizzlebeard – gold doubloons
Mumbles McGraw – pieces of eight
Scurvy Joe Jones – silverware
Scarface Jake – necklaces

Page 60

Captain Cutthroat

Page 62

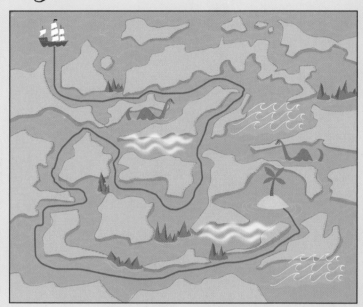

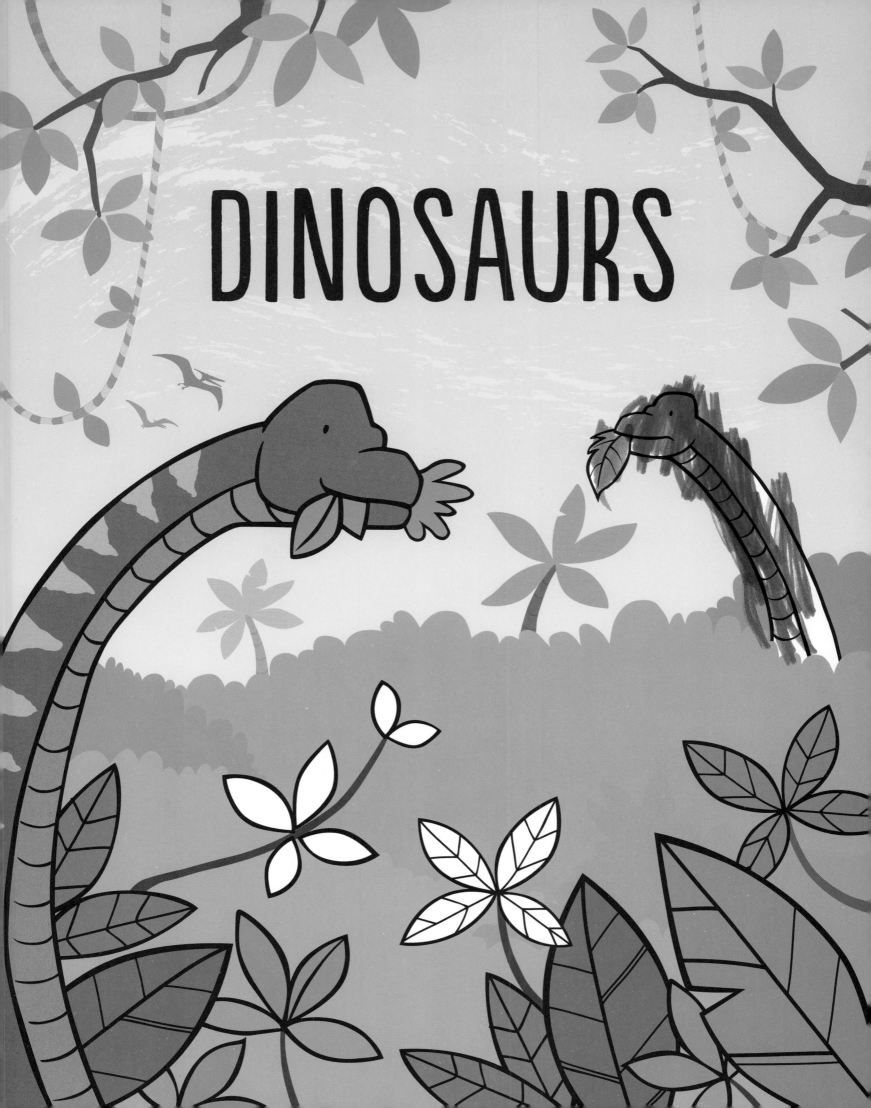

DINOSAURS

Dimetrodon (dim-EAT-rod-on)

The big creature here is a Dimetrodon. It's not actually a dinosaur, although it looks like one. Its legs were on the side of its body, not underneath, so it walked with a waddle. Dimetrodons lived millions of years before the first dinosaurs.

How to draw a Dimetrodon

Use a pencil to draw a large oval.

Then draw a smaller oval.

Add a triangle.

Add a curved line.

Draw four legs.

Add a face, and a zigzag line to the "sail" on its back.

Use a pen to draw around the outline of the body.

Plateosaurus (plat-ee-o-SORE-us)

Plateosauruses were plant-eating dinosaurs. They roamed around in herds, looking for trees. When they found some, they stood on their back legs, stretched out their necks, and munched on leaves that smaller creatures couldn't reach.

How to draw a Plateosaurus

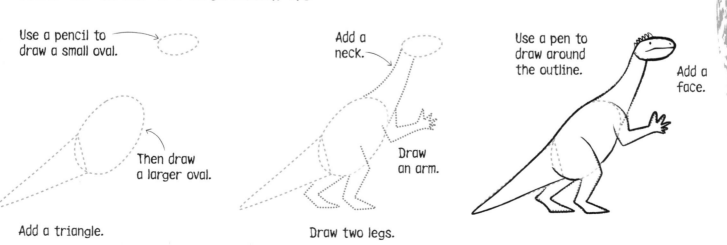

Use a pencil to draw a small oval.

Then draw a larger oval.

Add a triangle.

Add a neck.

Draw an arm.

Draw two legs.

Use a pen to draw around the outline.

Add a face.

Eoraptor (EE-oh-rap-ter)

Eoraptor was about the same size as a Labrador dog (but a lot less cuddly). It was light and fast, and ran after its prey on two legs. All the smaller animals were afraid of this nimble little dinosaur, with its large claws and nasty bite.

How to draw an Eoraptor

Use a pencil to draw half an oval.

Add a triangle.

Draw an oval.

Add a neck.

Draw two arms.

Draw two legs.

Use a pen to draw around the outline.

Draw a face and some sharp teeth.

Diplodocus (dih-PLOD-o-kus)

Diplodocus was a gigantic dinosaur. Its enormous neck allowed it to reach almost any leaf it liked, and it used its long, lashing tail to whip away its enemies. It may even have used its tail to help it swim across water.

How to draw a Diplodocus

Use a pencil to draw a large oval.

Then draw a smaller oval.

Add a long tail.

Add a long neck.

Draw four legs.

Use a pen to draw around the outline.

Add a face and toes.

Stegosaurus (steg-o-SORE-us)

Stegosaurus had pointed plates on its back that stuck up like two rows of terrifying teeth. The bigger its plates, the more popular a male Stegosaurus was with females, because large plates showed what a strong, healthy dinosaur it was.

How to draw a Stegosaurus

Use a pencil to draw a large oval.

Then draw a small oval.

Add a triangle.

Add two lines for the neck.

Draw some big pointed plates.

Draw four legs.

Use a pen to draw around the outline.

Add a face and toes.

Archaeopteryx (ark-ee-OP-ter-ix)

Archaeopteryx was a bird about the size of a chicken, but unlike modern birds, it had teeth. Archaeopteryx couldn't fly very well and it probably used its feathery wings to glide from branch to branch.

How to draw an Archaeopteryx

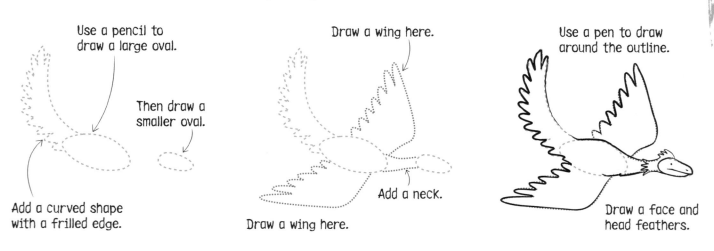

Use a pencil to draw a large oval.

Then draw a smaller oval.

Add a curved shape with a frilled edge.

Draw a wing here.

Add a neck.

Draw a wing here.

Use a pen to draw around the outline.

Draw a face and head feathers.

Plesiosaurus (plee-see-o-SORE-us)

Plesiosaurus was a huge sea creature that lived at the same time as the dinosaurs. It used its narrow flippers to paddle itself through the water, and darted its long, snake-like neck to and fro to catch fish in its tooth-filled jaws.

How to draw a Plesiosaurus

Use a pencil to draw a large oval.

Then draw a smaller oval.

Add a long neck.

Use a pen to draw around the outline.

Add a triangle.

Draw four flippers.

Add a face and teeth.

Ankylosaurus (ank-eye-lo-SORE-us)

Ankylosaurus was a plant-eating dinosaur. Its back was protected by a tough shield of bony plates, bumps and spikes embedded in its leathery skin. At the end of its tail was a bony club, which it probably swung at its enemies to defend itself.

How to draw an Ankylosaurus

Use a pencil to draw a large oval.

Then draw a smaller oval.

Add a neck.

Add a curved tail.

Add the tail club and back spikes.

Draw four legs.

Use a pen to draw around the outline.

Add a face and lots more spikes.

Tyrannosaurus rex (tih-ran-o-SORE-us rex)

Tyrannosaurus rex was a ferocious meat-eating dinosaur with a huge head, and powerful jaws for crushing its prey. Its legs were strong, so it could probably chase its victims quickly for short distances.

How to draw a Tyrannosaurus rex

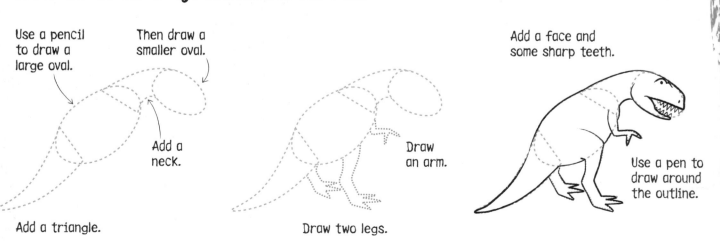

Use a pencil to draw a large oval.

Then draw a smaller oval.

Add a face and some sharp teeth.

Add a neck.

Draw an arm.

Use a pen to draw around the outline.

Add a triangle.

Draw two legs.

Pteranodon (teh-RAN-o-don)

Pteranodons were flying creatures that lived in prehistoric times. They used their leathery wings to glide through the air. They had no teeth, so when they caught a fish in their beak, they probably tipped back their head and swallowed it whole.

How to draw a Pteranodon

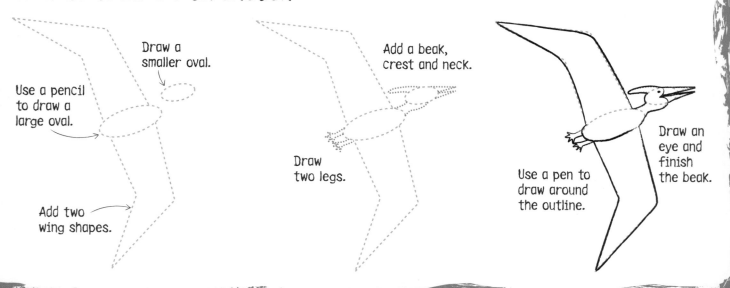

Draw a smaller oval.

Use a pencil to draw a large oval.

Add two wing shapes.

Add a beak, crest and neck.

Draw two legs.

Use a pen to draw around the outline.

Draw an eye and finish the beak.

Triceratops (try-SERA-tops)

Triceratops was a plant-eating dinosaur. It was about the size of an elephant, and a large bony frill on its head made it look even bigger. Horns as long and thick as an adult's leg, and a sharp, parrot-like beak helped it fight off enemies.

How to draw a Triceratops

Use a pencil to draw a large oval.

Then draw a smaller oval.

Add a triangle.

Add a nose, three horns and a frill.

Draw four legs.

Use a pen to draw around the outline.

Add a face and toes.

Maiasaura (my-a-SORE-a)

Like all dinosaur mothers, Maiasaura females laid eggs with their babies inside. They dug holes in the ground to lay their eggs in, then watched over their newly hatched babies until they were strong enough to leave their nest.

How to draw a Maiasaura

Use a pencil to draw a large oval.

Then draw a smaller oval.

Add a curve along the back.

Add a snout.

Use a pen to draw around the outline.

Add a triangle.

Add a neck.

Draw four legs.

Draw a face.

Parasaurolophus (para-sore-OL-o-fuss)

Parasaurolophus had a tall, hollow crest on its head. Scientists think the dinosaur may have sucked in air through its nose and up into its crest, making a loud, deep noise. It may have sounded like a honking foghorn echoing around the forest.

How to draw a Parasaurolophus

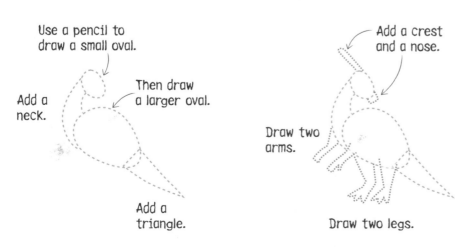

Use a pencil to draw a small oval.

Then draw a larger oval.

Add a neck.

Add a triangle.

Add a crest and a nose.

Draw two arms.

Draw two legs.

Use a pen to draw around the outline.

Draw a face.

Spinosaurus (spy-no-SORE-us)

Spinosaurus was probably the largest meat-eating dinosaur of all time. It was longer than a bus, and had a fin on its back as tall as a person. Its crocodile-like snout bristled with savage teeth, which it used to spear fish, and other dinosaurs.

How to draw a Spinosaurus

Use a pencil to draw a large oval.

Then draw a smaller oval.

Add a neck.

Add a curved hook for the tail.

Add the large fin.

Draw two arms.

Draw two legs.

Use a pen to draw around the outline.

Add a face and lots of teeth.

Dinosaur skeletons

Dinosaurs died out long before people existed, but their bones were buried in the ground, where they turned to stone. Scientists have pieced these together like giant jigsaw puzzles, to build skeletons that give us a clue to what different dinosaurs looked like. The dinosaur skeleton in this picture is a Stegosaurus.

How to draw a Stegosaurus skeleton

Use a pencil to draw a small oval.

Then draw a long back bone.

Add rib bones.

Add lots of pointed plates, like these.

Draw four leg bones.

Use a pen to draw around the outline.

Add an eye hole, a mouth and toe bones.

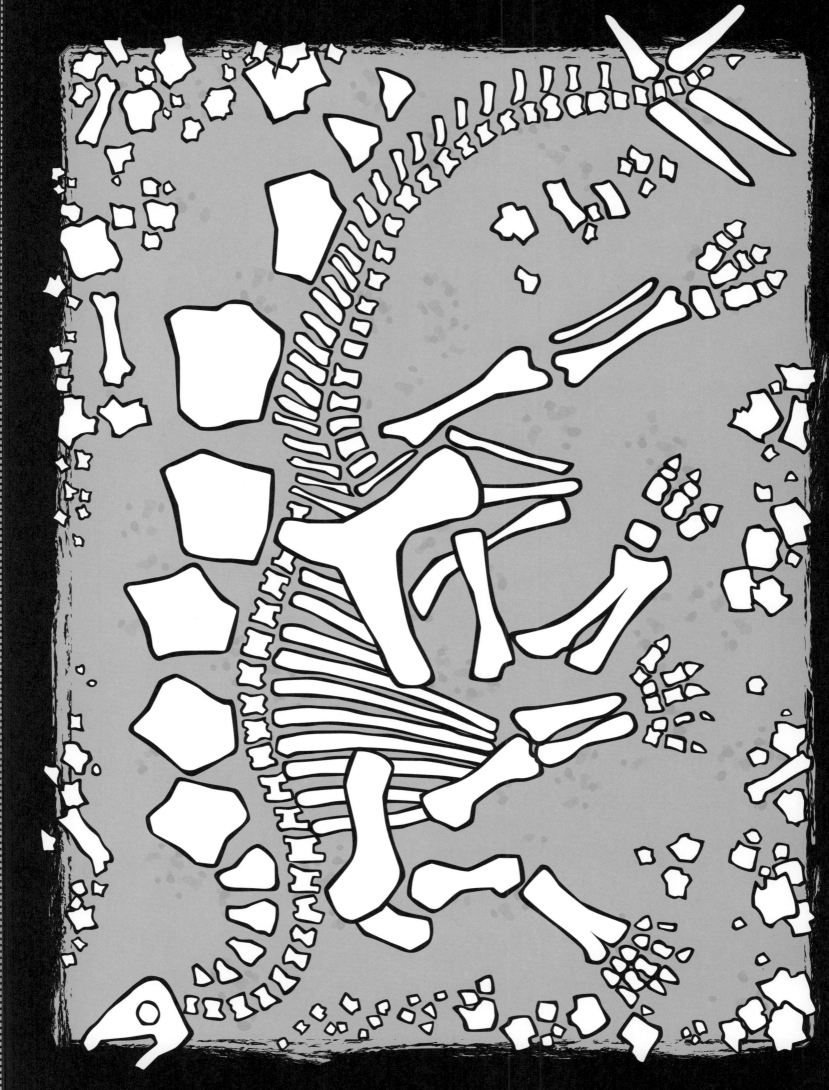

Patterned dinosaurs

No one knows what color dinosaurs were, and they may have had all kinds of patterns. Fill these dinosaurs with the boldest patterns you can draw – you can use zigzags, spots, stripes and squiggles.

KNIGHTS & CASTLES

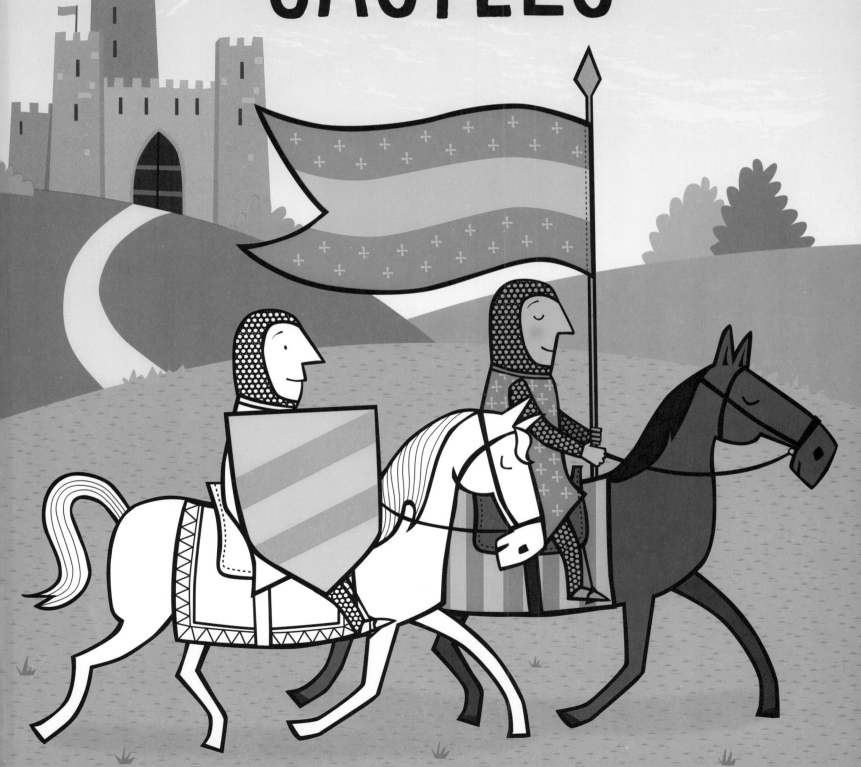

Weapon store

Knights were trained fighting men who rode horses. In battle, they most often used swords and long poles called lances to defend themselves against opponents wielding a wide variety of vicious weapons.

There were many different types of swords, with strong metal blades that could be used to slash, hack or stab an enemy.

Battle axes were used for swiping at enemies or throwing at them from a distance.

Daggers were small, narrow knives, useful for finding small gaps in an opponent's armor.

A flail was swung at the enemy. The spiked iron ball could catch on a knight's armor to help pull him from his horse.

Spiked metal caltrops were scattered on the ground to hurt the feet of enemy soldiers and horses.

Maces were sturdy sticks with heavy metal ends. A hefty mace blow could crush a suit of armor, and the knight inside it.

This is a lance. A knight on horseback would carry it tucked under his arm, and use it to stab an enemy or knock him off his horse.

Dreadful dragons

There are lots of stories about knights fighting terrifying dragons.
One of the most famous tales is about St. George and the Dragon.

Here's a space for you to draw a dragon of your own.

How to draw a dragon

Use a pencil to
draw a large
oval.

Add a
neck.

Add a long
triangle.

Draw a
triangle.

Draw a wing.

Add two legs.

Draw
an arm.

Use a pen to draw
around the outline.

Add lots
of spikes.

Draw a face
and sharp
teeth.

A fabulous feast

The richest knights owned castles. They often hosted lavish feasts, with menus that included roasted peacocks, stuffed swans and succulent pies, marzipan castles, honeycakes and other luxury desserts. A procession of pages paraded the dishes in front of the guests before the food was cut up and served.

Make up a magnificent menu for a feast in the space below.

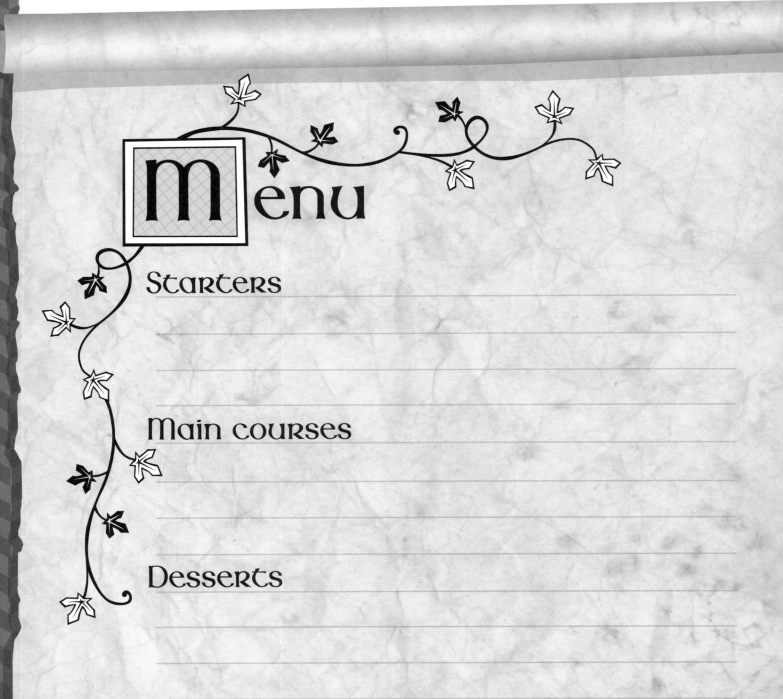

Menu

Starters

Main courses

Desserts

At the joust

In a joust, a pair of knights on horseback charged towards one another, each trying to hit the other with his lance. Some knights wore special jousting helmets. They had to lower their head to see through the narrow slit, but then lifted it again just before they clashed, to protect their eyes. Knights often decorated their helmets for the occasion.

This helmet is decorated with feathers.

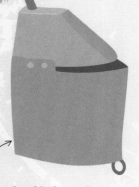

This helmet has horns made from boiled leather on it. A wreath of twisted silks (called a torse) is in the main colors of the knight's coat of arms.

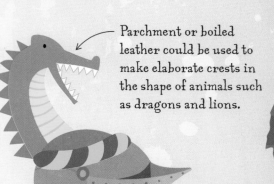

Parchment or boiled leather could be used to make elaborate crests in the shape of animals such as dragons and lions.

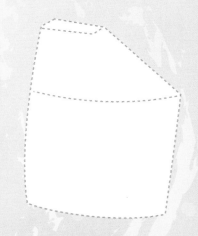

Late 15th-century helmet

This style of helmet, known as a great helm, was fashionable for several hundred years.

Mid 15th-century helmet

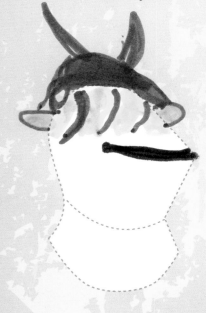

Finish these helmets, adding eye slits and fancy crests on the top.

Getting dressed

Putting on armor was a complicated business and knights had young helpers called squires to assist them.

Draw some armor on the knight, to get him ready for battle.

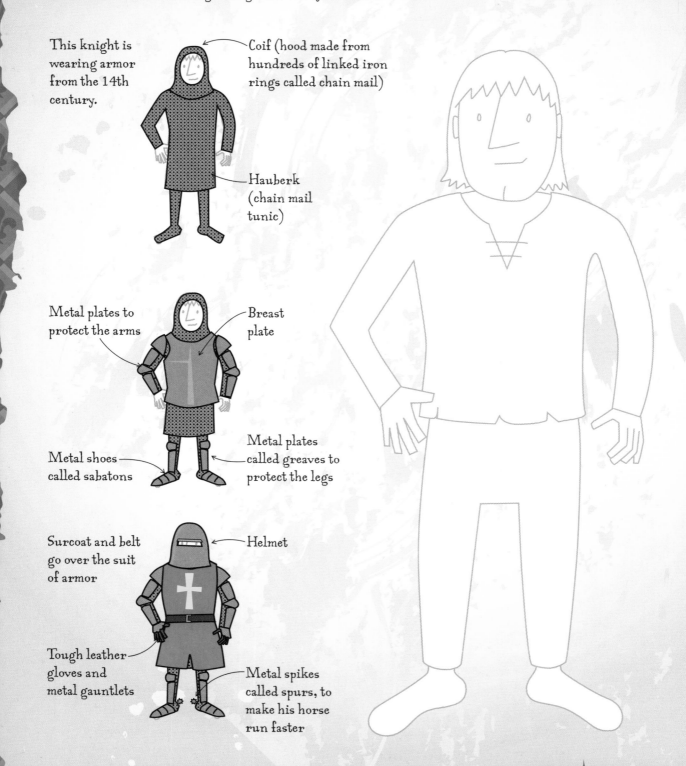

This knight is wearing armor from the 14th century.

Coif (hood made from hundreds of linked iron rings called chain mail)

Hauberk (chain mail tunic)

Metal plates to protect the arms

Breast plate

Metal shoes called sabatons

Metal plates called greaves to protect the legs

Surcoat and belt go over the suit of armor

Helmet

Tough leather gloves and metal gauntlets

Metal spikes called spurs, to make his horse run faster

Turrets and towers

Castles looked different depending where and when they were built, from a single square tower, to ring after ring of towers and walls.

Add towers and turrets to the picture to design a castle of your own.

Under attack!

Sometimes enemies tried to take over a knight's castle. One way was to camp outside it, stopping supplies and starving people into surrender. But it was quicker to use force, and there were many tactics they could use.

Finish the pictures below and find out more.

Attackers used huge wooden shields to protect them as they moved within firing range of the castle.

Giant wooden catapults fired missiles such as heavy rocks at the castle walls. Sometimes enemies flung dead animals over the walls, to spread disease.

Add some wet animal skins to help stop the ram from catching fire.

A battering ram is a frame with a large tree trunk inside it. Soldiers swung this against walls, doors and gates to bring them crashing down.

Enemies used long scaling ladders to climb the castle walls, but the ladders could be pushed away, and soldiers had no protection while they climbed.

Wooden siege towers full of soldiers could be pushed up to the castle. A drop-down bridge at the top let them climb onto the walls. Draw more soldiers inside the tower.

Going hunting

In their spare time, knights enjoyed hunting animals such as deer, boars, bears and wolves. A hunt was a great social event as well as a way to put meat on the menu. Once the hunting dogs had picked up an animal's scent, knights, ladies and huntsmen joined in the chase.

You could draw your own horse picture here.

How to draw a horse

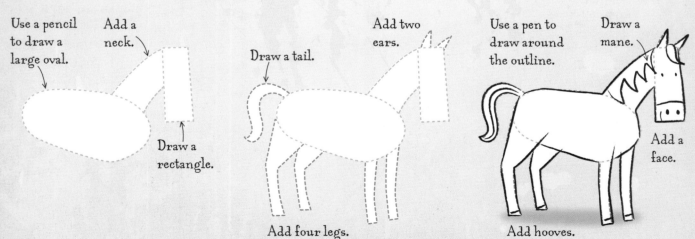

Use a pencil to draw a large oval.

Add a neck.

Draw a rectangle.

Draw a tail.

Add four legs.

Add two ears.

Use a pen to draw around the outline.

Draw a mane.

Add a face.

Add hooves.

On the battlefield

At the start of a battle, knights lined up, shoulder to shoulder on horseback, with their lances pointing towards the enemy. On the signal, they charged forwards to attack. A knight who lost his horse had to finish the fight on foot.

Draw some fighting knights.

How to draw a knight

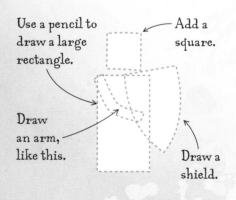

Use a pencil to draw a large rectangle.

Add a square.

Draw an arm, like this.

Draw a shield.

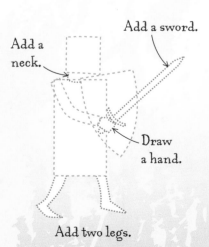

Add a neck.

Add a sword.

Draw a hand.

Add two legs.

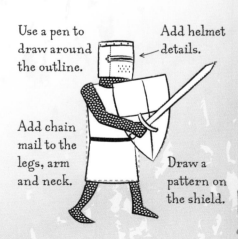

Use a pen to draw around the outline.

Add helmet details.

Add chain mail to the legs, arm and neck.

Draw a pattern on the shield.

Knight school

Boys from noble families were often sent to a knight's castle to train as knights. They started as pages, fetching, carrying and learning good manners. Later, as squires, they took care of the knight's horses and armor, and continued to learn the skills they'd need in battle.

Read about some of the skills a page would learn.

Pages practiced with blunt wooden swords, and small round shields called bucklers, so they didn't hurt each other.

This page is sitting astride a wooden horse, trying to hit the target with his dummy lance. He's learning how to control a lance while keeping his balance in the saddle.

These boys are pretending to joust. They have one long stick between their legs as a horse, and another under their arms as a lance.

Wrestling helped pages become strong and fit. Piggyback fighting helped them develop the balance they would need to fight on horseback.

Coats of arms

Each knight had a design, called a coat of arms, painted on his shield to identify him in battle. Over time, knights put their coats of arms on all kinds of things from clothes to tournament tents. In a tournament a knight might also wear a token, such as a handkerchief, from a lady he wanted to impress.

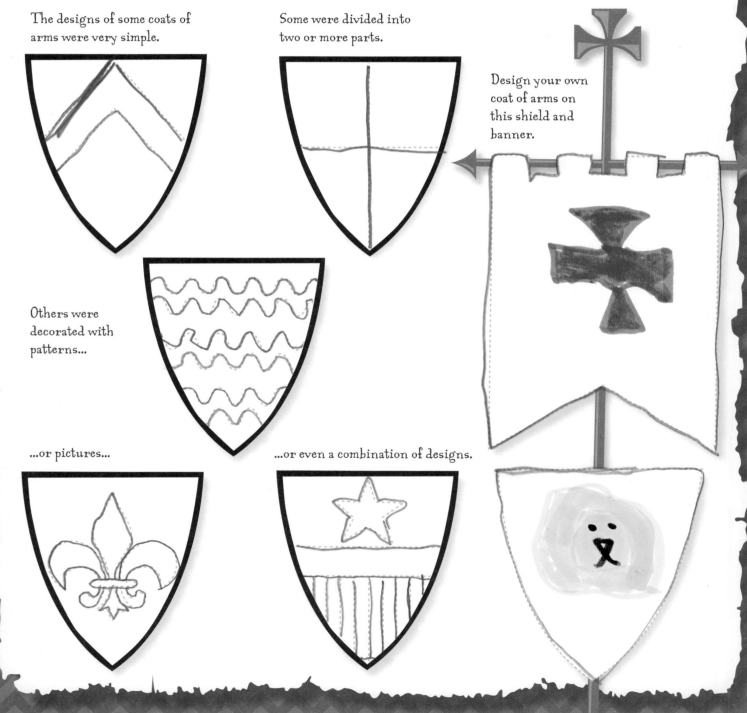

The designs of some coats of arms were very simple.

Some were divided into two or more parts.

Design your own coat of arms on this shield and banner.

Others were decorated with patterns...

...or pictures...

...or even a combination of designs.

Knight to the rescue

A knight was expected to be chivalrous. This meant being brave and loyal, protecting the weak and treating his enemies fairly. There are lots of tales about knights rescuing princesses from danger.

You could use this space to write your own story.

Once upon a time there was a very ROYOL knight named Sir SOLON MARTENES He lived IN Ah Blieg Cad Grogon lang hi WAS HAPPY

One day he was out riding when hi saw ah bikutafol prinsec dey WANTED Tu bi Tu petr but dor WAS ah wicne ho gardo da krensec hi chrgod hi wos sow klosg but den da wicha Irng in tow ah Drogon hi Chrgo den da prinse bntde swish histeda and da prinses livda

The End

Castle life

Most bigger castles had a wide courtyard called a bailey inside them, where the servants worked and lived. Below you can find out about some of the buildings you might have seen inside the castle walls.

Finish drawing the pictures and add your own details.

The kitchens

The kennels

A fletcher's workshop

Knights kept dogs as pets, and for hunting with, to provide fresh meat. Hunting hounds lived in the kennels.

The kitchens were separate from the castle. They had stone roofs, to stop flames from the cooking setting them alight. Draw a cooking pot over a fire.

Fletchers made wooden shafts for arrows, and the flights (end feathers). Draw some arrows here.

The stables

The bakery

The stables housed the knight's destriers (war horses), palfreys for everyday riding and coursers for hunting. There were ladies' horses too, and packhorses for carrying baggage and carthorses for pulling wagons. Add more horses to the stables.

Bread was made in large stone ovens. There was white bread for guests and brown for servants. Draw some round loaves of bread.

Arise, Sir Knight

An experienced squire, who had mastered the fighting skills he needed, was ready to become a knight. This was done in a knighting ceremony performed by a senior knight, or sometimes even by the king himself. Once a squire had been knighted, he was called 'Sir.'

Read about the stages of a knighting ceremony, then see if you can put them in the correct order. You'll find the answer at the bottom of page 132.

A
During the ceremony, the king or senior knight tapped the kneeling squire on the shoulders with a sword or a glove. This was called dubbing.

B
On the evening before the ceremony, the squire had a bath. As well as getting clean, it was a symbol that his thoughts were pure, and worthy of a knight.

C
In the morning, other squires helped the squire to dress in new clothes – another symbol of purity, and his new life as a knight.

D
Finally, the knight went back to the chapel to be blessed by a priest. The ceremony was often followed by a big feast with music and dancing.

E
After bathing, the squire went to the chapel. He spent the night thinking about his new role and praying that he would be a good and noble knight.

F
The new knight was given a sword and spurs (heel spikes to make his horse run faster), and other symbols of his new position.

Wall of fame

The bravery and skill of some knights made them famous and gave them a place in history. You can see pictures of some of them on the page opposite.

Why not draw and name your own knight on the wall hanging below?

RODRIGO DÍAZ DE VIVAR (EL CID)
c.1043~1099

A legendary Spanish knight who fought for both the
Christians and the Muslims in religious wars known
as the Crusades. He was famous for never losing a battle.

Salah al Din Yusuf ibn Ayyub (Saladin)
1138 ~ 1193

A clever Muslim leader who fought in the
religious wars known as the Crusades.
His chivalry, bravery and strong
faith were even admired by the
Christians he was fighting.

KING ARTHUR

A very famous knight, although he may not really
have existed. Stories say he ruled from a place called
Camelot, and led a band of brave knights who became
known as the Knights of the Round Table. Two of his
best knights are pictured in the oval frames below.

JOAN OF ARC
1412-1431

Joan of Arc was a young French woman who helped
the Dauphin (the heir to the French throne) fight
against the English, and she even led the French
armies to victory in several battles. In 1430 she was
taken prisoner by the English, accused of having
unacceptable religious views and put to death. She
became a French heroine and was later made a saint.

SIR LANCELOT

SIR GALAHAD

EDWARD THE BLACK PRINCE
c.1330-1376

Edward was knighted at
the age of 15. He famously
defeated 18,000 French
soldiers with just 7,000
men at the Battle of
Poitiers in 1356.

Swordsmanship

Knights prided themselves on their swordsmanship, which was tested both in tournaments and on the battlefield. Color these knights, and decide which one is likely to win.

MONSTERS

Howling werewolves

As a bright, full moon rises over Creepy Canyon, the eerie yowling of a lone werewolf echoes across the emptiness. Suddenly another chilling howl answers the call, followed by another... and then another...

Here's a space for you to add a fourth fearsome werewolf to the pack – half man and half wolf, armed with razor-sharp claws.

How to draw a werewolf

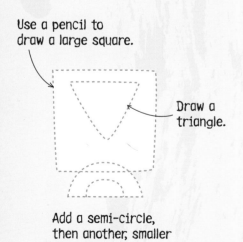

Use a pencil to draw a large square.

Draw a triangle.

Add a semi-circle, then another, smaller one inside.

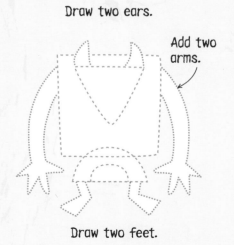

Draw two ears.

Add two arms.

Draw two feet.

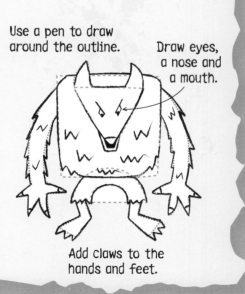

Use a pen to draw around the outline.

Draw eyes, a nose and a mouth.

Add claws to the hands and feet.

Monster in the city

Run for your life! An angry monster is rampaging through the city, bulldozing buildings, tearing up trees and crushing cars. Finish the cityscape below, adding sleek skyscrapers and a few toppling towers. You could draw some cars, buses or trains too if you like.

Swamp monster

In the great, green, greasy marshes lurks a hideous beast.
Covered in sludge and slime, the swamp monster lies in wait
for anyone who stumbles into its boggy den. Give this monster
eyes and a mouth, then draw some drips and other dribbly details.

Loch Ness Monster

Many look for it, a few claim to have seen it, but does it really exist? Is there an ancient McMonster living in the deep, dark waters of this Scottish Loch, or is it just a floating log, mistaken in the mists?

Draw your own "Nessie" in the space below.

How to draw "Nessie"

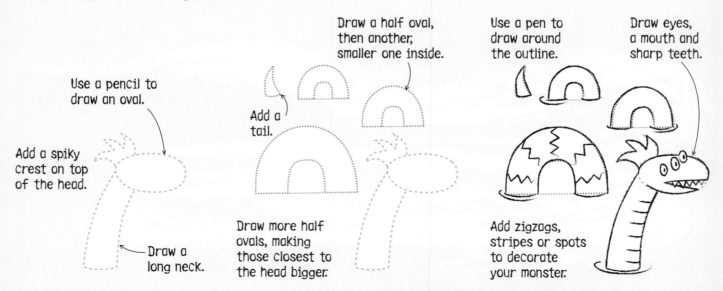

Use a pencil to draw an oval.

Add a spiky crest on top of the head.

Draw a long neck.

Add a tail.

Draw more half ovals, making those closest to the head bigger.

Draw a half oval, then another, smaller one inside.

Use a pen to draw around the outline.

Add zigzags, stripes or spots to decorate your monster.

Draw eyes, a mouth and sharp teeth.

Hungry monster

RRRaaaarrrr! What deafening rumbles are thundering from this monster's tummy!
He is raiding the pantry and will eat anything in his path to satisfy his hunger.
Write a menu for a mighty meal that a ravenous monster might like to munch.

Monster menu

Starters o _____

_____

_____

_____

Main courses _____

_____

_____

_____

_____

Desserts _____

_____

_____

_____

Mini-monsters

Not all monsters are big, bold and brash – some are nasty little critters, so small that you might easily miss them. Create your own monster mini-beast garden by adding eyes, bodies and nippy gnashers to the shapes below.

Monster mug shots

This motley collection of criminals is wanted by the department of Monster Control for all sorts of mischief. Have you seen them? Read their Grime Squad files, then finish the identity cards below, based on the descriptions and pictures.

MONSTER CONTROL

Suspect: IC-U8-9X-4T

Fingerprint found at 112 Acacia Drive

MONSTER CONTROL

Grumpy bumpy

MONSTER CONTROL
SPOTTY McDOTTY
USING SOAP

MONSTER CONTROL
SOCK MONSTER
REUNITING ODD SOCKS IN THE LAUNDRY

MONSTER CONTROL

slime atack

MONSTER CONTROL

TARANTULA GARGANTULA

RUNNING FROM A SCREAMING CHILD

MONSTER CONTROL

EVIL EYEBALL

BLINKING UNDER PRESSURE

MONSTER CONTROL

MUMMY MONSTER

FAILING TO MOAN

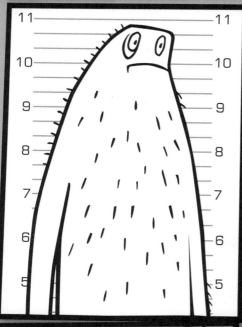

MONSTER CONTROL

DOPPLE CLANGER

RANDOM ACTS OF KINDNESS

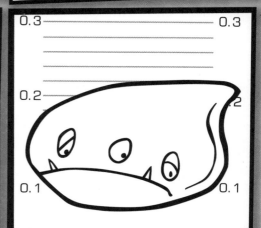

MONSTER CONTROL

BEASTIE BLUBBER BLOB

ALLOWING HIMSELF
TO BE FLUSHED AWAY

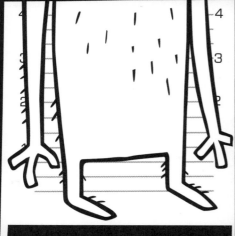

MONSTER CONTROL

TICKLE MONSTER

WARMING HANDS BEFORE DUTY

MONSTER CONTROL

MUNCHER CRUNCHER

GOING ON A DIET

MONSTER CONTROL

BRIAN

USING AN
UN-MONSTERLY NAME

Terrible troll

Some fairytales and legends tell of ugly monsters called trolls that live in dark, damp places - under dank bridges or in deep mountain caves. Some stories say that even a ray of sunlight turns them to stone. Trolls are incredibly strong, but rather smelly, slow and not very bright.

Draw some gruesome ingredients in the troll stew below. The stinkier and more revolting they look, the better.

Monsters under the bed

Tired out by a day of naughtiness, sneaky Spike falls asleep. Almost at once, there's a rustle, then a groan, and one by one all kinds of monsters creep out from under his bed. There's Boggle-eyes the bookworm, and Snatch the thief, Moping Murgatroyd, and the tiresome Two-headed Tweak...

You could use this space to write a story about what they did.

"Hey!" said Boggle-eyes, "Give that book back!"
"Won't!" said Snatch, his . . . .
eyes glinting. "I want to look at the . . . .
. . . .
. . . .
. . . .
. . . .
. . . .
. . . .
. . . .

The end

Alien monsters

Far out in space there may be all kinds of creatures, far stranger than anyone can imagine. Draw your own aliens in the spaceships below. There is space for you to design a spacecraft too.

Monsters in the attic

The attic is alive with mischievous monsters – mix-up monsters who move things and brittle monsters who break things. Continue filling this attic room with junk. Then, add your own meddlesome monsters hiding amid the mess.

Frankenstein's monster

Victor Frankenstein was a character in a storybook. He was an inventor who longed to find the secret of life. After years of experiments he built a creature out of spare parts and jolted it into life with a lightning flash. But his lumbering creation was so ugly that everyone feared it, and the lonely monster lived an empty life of bitter revenge.

How to draw Frankenstein's monster

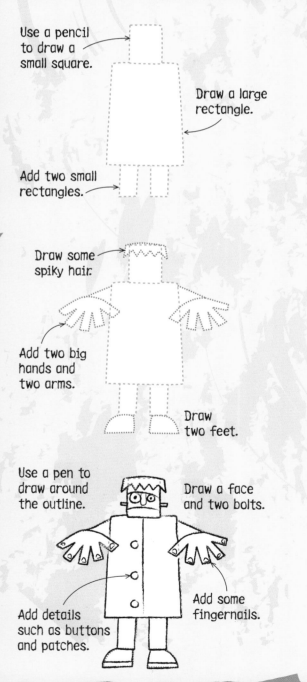

Use a pencil to draw a small square.

Draw a large rectangle.

Add two small rectangles.

Draw some spiky hair.

Add two big hands and two arms.

Draw two feet.

Use a pen to draw around the outline.

Draw a face and two bolts.

Add details such as buttons and patches.

Add some fingernails.

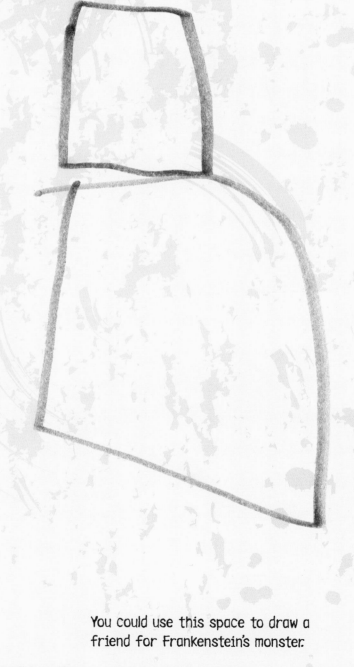

You could use this space to draw a friend for Frankenstein's monster.

Monster gallery

You don't have to go far to find a story with a monster in it. On the page opposite you can read about some famous monsters in myths and legends.

You could draw your own monster in the frame below. If you like, you could write about it too, for example, what is it called, what does it guard, and how can it be defeated?

HYDRA

In Greek myths, the Hydra was a terrible monster that lived in a dreary swamp. The creature had nine serpent-like heads which belched out billowing clouds of poison. A hero named Hercules was tasked to tackle the terror, but each time he swiped one of its heads with his club, two new heads grew in its place. His nephew used burning branches to set fire to its necks, and as the last head tumbled to the ground, so the Hydra was slain.

Dracula

Count Dracula is a vampire character in a book by Bram Stoker. Vampires are legendary monsters that steal life by drinking their victims' blood. They can be held at bay by garlic, holy water and the sign of the cross, which they cannot bear. But the only way to destroy a vampire is to drive a sharp wooden stake through its heart.

MANTICORE

This mythical monster from ancient Persia had the body of a lion, the head of a human, and three rows of savage teeth. It devoured its prey whole.

THE GOLEM

Golems are hulking creatures from Jewish legend, shaped from clay and brought to life by magic. The most famous one was the Golem of Prague.

Medusa

In Greek myths, Medusa was a hideous monster with seething snakes for hair. Anyone who looked at her turned to stone. A hero named Perseus sought her out and, by watching her reflection in his shiny shield, cut off her head.

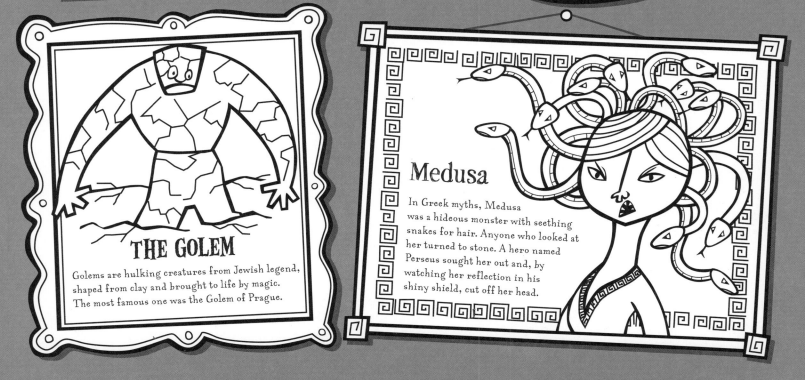

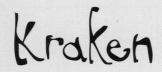

Kraken

Kraken are legendary sea monsters that were once said to lurk in the chilly waters near Norway. Early accounts tell how these ocean giants reared up out of the waves, their thick tentacles thrashing, before sinking into the deep, leaving a whirl of rushing waters that sucked helpless ships down to their doom.

Add more long, lashing legs to this Kraken, then doodle some whirling waves around it.

The Minotaur

The Minotaur was a terrible monster in Ancient Greek myths. Half bull and half man, it lurked at the heart of a labyrinth (a huge maze), devouring anyone who entered its lair. Eventually, a brave hero named Theseus destroyed the Minotaur, then escaped from the labyrinth by following a trail of enchanted twine.

Use your pencil to help Theseus find his way out of the labyrinth.

Monster party

Make these party monsters as colorful and patterned as can be. Zigzags, spots, stars and dots, rainbow stripes and zany party outfits – nothing is too bright for a monster party!

SOCCER

Soccer uniform

Use the blank shirt below to design
your very own soccer shirt.

Match-day travel

Soccer fans travel far and wide to watch their team play. Add faces to the fans in the cars below and draw some more supporters in the bus.

Training session

As well as being super fit, soccer players need to work hard to perfect their technique. These players are practicing different skills. For each one, decide where you think the ball should be, and draw it in.

using the inside
of the foot

using the knee

using the head

the heel catch

using the instep
(top of the foot)

using the chest

Hall of fame

Everyman United's hall of fame is full of photos of its star players, past and present. Add your own soccer heroes to the gallery, by cutting and sticking pictures from magazines or newspapers, or drawing them, in the frames below.

ALEX CLARKE • Goalkeeper of the year • 1982

Club Founder
Members
Edward Thomas
Archibald Robinson

Fernando Fereira
Current team captain

Hall of Fame

WAYNE WESTON Top goal scorer 1978

THOMAS ROBSON Captain of Cup-winning team 2009

Alfred Thompson
Soccer League 1888

Everyman United Soccer Club • 1907

Players: Archie Advantage (Captain), Bartholomew Boot, Victor Volley, Peter Penalty, Terence Tackle, Wesley Winger,
Frankie Freekick, Ronald Relegation, Harry Hamstring, Bernard Backswing, Morris Midfield, Oscar Offside.
Manager: Derek Dribble

Team line-up

The manager has picked his team for today's match. Create your own ideal line-up by cutting soccer players' faces from newspapers or magazines and sticking them onto the heads below. Or if you want to, you can draw faces in the spaces to complete your winning side, and color in the shirts.

Cheering crowd

The fans are having a great time watching their side play.
Design your own banner and flags below to cheer on your team.

Super skills

Write down your dream teams on the manager's clipboard below. Choose carefully – remember you need a range of skills on the soccer field, not just great goalscorers. You could choose one team of family and friends, and one with soccer stars.

Manager's Dream Teams

Soccer stars	Friends and family
★ 1	
★ 2	
★ 3	
★ 4	
★ 5	
★ 6	
★ 7	
★ 8	
★ 9	
★ 10	
★ 11	

Free kick

These players are practicing some fancy footwork. Draw in their legs to match the position of the balls.

Half-time hunger

Hordes of hungry fans are lining up for hot dogs and drinks. Cut and stick pictures from magazines or newspapers of things that you'd like to eat to give you energy for shouting and cheering in the second half.

Harry's Hot Food and Drinks

Hot Drinks
Cold Drinks
Burgers
Bacon Bagels
Hot Dogs
Premium Pies

Tomato Ketchup
Barbecue Sauce

Goal!

He shoots. He scores! Draw in the goalkeeper between the posts – it's up to you whether it's a goal or a save. The first one has been done for you.

Foul!

A bad tackle has made front-page news. Make up names of the teams and players to finish off the article below, then add a picture.

SPORTS NEWS TODAY

SOCCER SPECIAL

FOUL PLAY

.... has been stretchered off only thirteen minutes into his debut for .... The big money signing had barely touched the ball before he was sent sprawling by a reckless tackle from ....

.... The two-footed lunge earned the .... midfielder a straight red card, but all eyes were on his victim. A spokesman for the club has said the player should be fit for the game against .... in four weeks' time. This news will come as a relief for fans fearing a much longer layoff for their new star striker. The game itself ended in a goalless draw, with no one from either team able to provide the moment of magic that would have broken the deadlock. The man to do it was lying in a hospital bed.

Exclusive

NEW DEAL BETTER FOR MILES

Upandcoming City defender Miles Better has put pen to paper on a new contract that will tie him to Beesknees United for the next four years.

The talented midfielder made his international debut last month, and has carried on where he left off last season. He set up the winner against Wandering Rovers yesterday with a trademark defense-splitting pass that is fast ... is calling card.

HUBBLE AT THE DOUBL[

Roderigo Hubble continued his fine ... to the season with a man of the ... performance against Glebe County ... swashbuckling run cut through the C... defense in the fifty-second minut... he kept a cool head to slot past ... Folkes. With ten minutes left on th... he planted a powerful header in... post to confirm the win for Cornba... takes his tally for the season to fiv... games, and moves his club to to... ... ... behind th...

Penalty save

There are lots of ways a goalkeeper can stop
the ball. Some of them are shown below. For each
position, draw in where you think the ball should be.

high shot

punch

body shot

ground shot

palming

diving

We are the champions!

It's the end of the season, and Blackbridge United have won the Cup. Fill this page with fizzing fireworks to celebrate.

Trophy cabinet

Design a prizewinner's cup in the space below,
then write the champion's name on the plaque.

The winners!

Congratulations! Your team is ranked number 1 and is this year's league champion. Everyone is clapping and cheering at the victory parade. Finish filling in the rankings chart below, showing your team at the top.

No.	Team name	Jerseys	No.	Team name	Jerseys
1.	_____ _____		6.	_____ _____	
2.	_____ _____		7.	_____ _____	
3.	_____ _____		8.	_____ _____	
4.	_____ _____		9.	_____ _____	
5.	_____ _____		10.	Stripes_____ United_____	

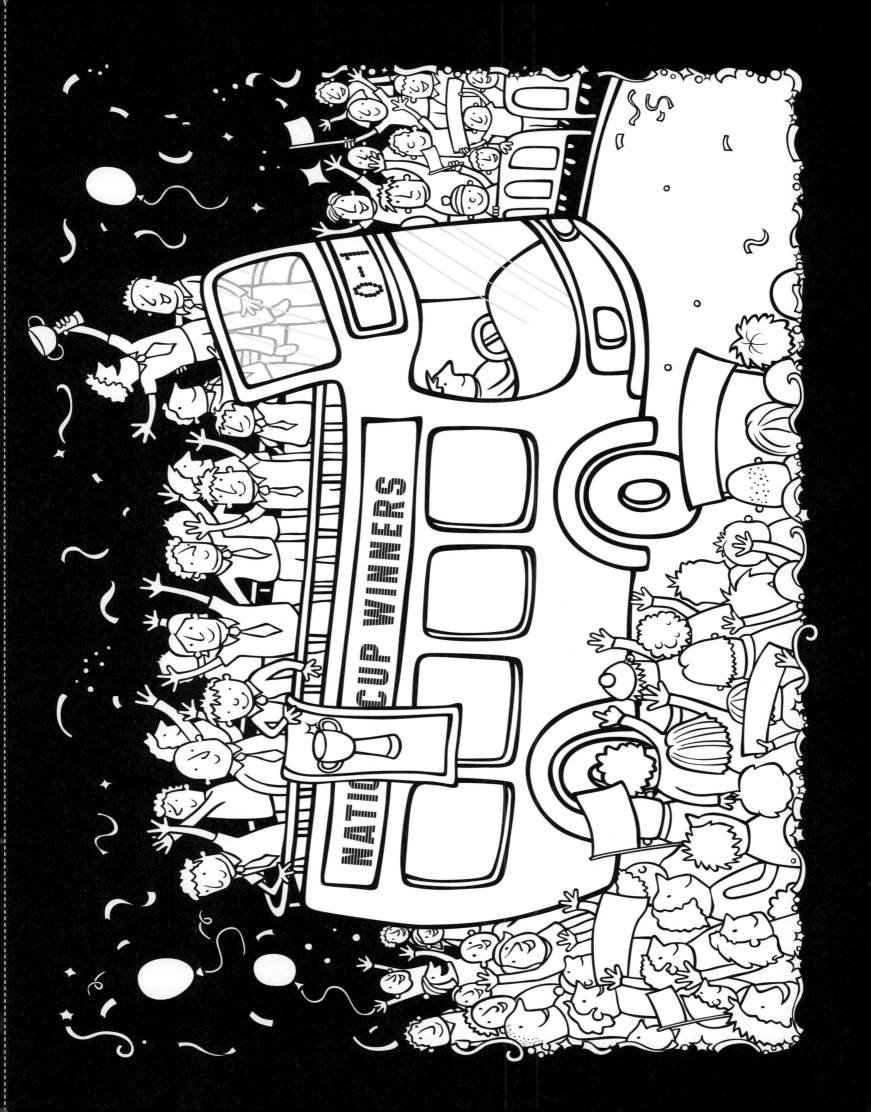

Lap of honor

These soccer players are doing a lap of honor after winning their last home game of the season. Give them suitably winning colors.

SPOOKY

R.I.P.

Here lies poor
Cousin
FRED
Struck by lightning
Now we dead

Here lies
Billy Sparks

A good father,
a loving husband,

but a terrible
electrician.

Here lies
the body of

Jonathan Blake

He stepped on the gas
Instead of the brake.

Cousin Jim

He loved crocodiles.
But the crocodiles
didn't love him.

Spooky portraits

The paintings are watching you! Draw your
own creepy character in the frame below.
Make him as scary as you like.

COUNT CRISPIN
(1655 - 1905)

Finger buffet

Create your own slimy snacks, nasty nibbles and septic soup on the cracked dishes provided.

Witching hour

It's midnight and wild-haired witches are zipping
and zooming through the sky on crooked broomsticks.
Sketch in some witchy shapes in front of this Moon.
You could add some bats and cats as well.

Pumpkin head

Design a scary face for your
very own pumpkin lantern.

Magical supplies

Fill the jars and bottles with putrid potions and poisonous powders. Draw over the dotted lines to finish stocking your spooky store.

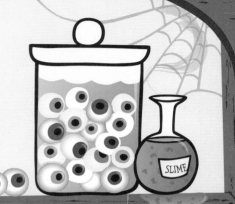

EXTRA JUICY WORMS
IN DITCH WATER

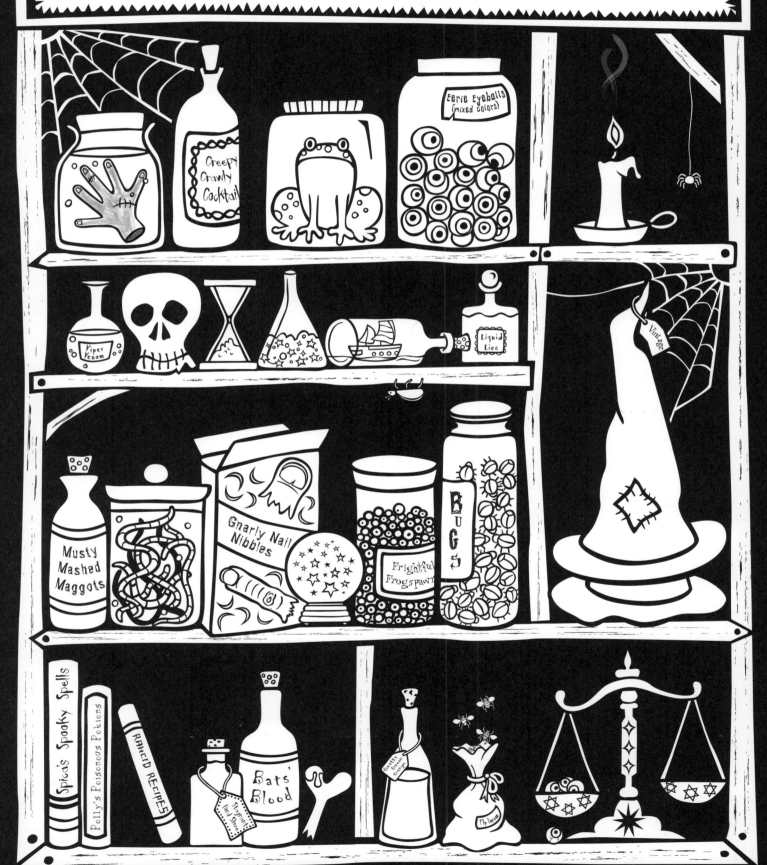

Horror movie

Septimus Snail and his slimy chums are watching scary movies on the TV again. Draw over the dotted lines, then sketch a scene or character from a hair-raising movie.

Haunted house

Turn this silhouette into a haunted house by adding creaky stairs, crooked windows, tumble-down towers and rickety roofs.

Grisly graves

These tombstones belong to Izzy A. Werewolf and Albie Back. Write their dates and details, then add a few cracks and cobwebs to complete the eerie effect.

Pesky plants

Fill the pots with ferocious ferns, deadly dandelions, biting buttercups and other perilous plants.

Creepy critters

There has been a new delivery at the Creepy Critters pet shop. Draw the ugliest pet you can imagine in the cage below. You could add some more cage bars, to stop your creature from escaping.

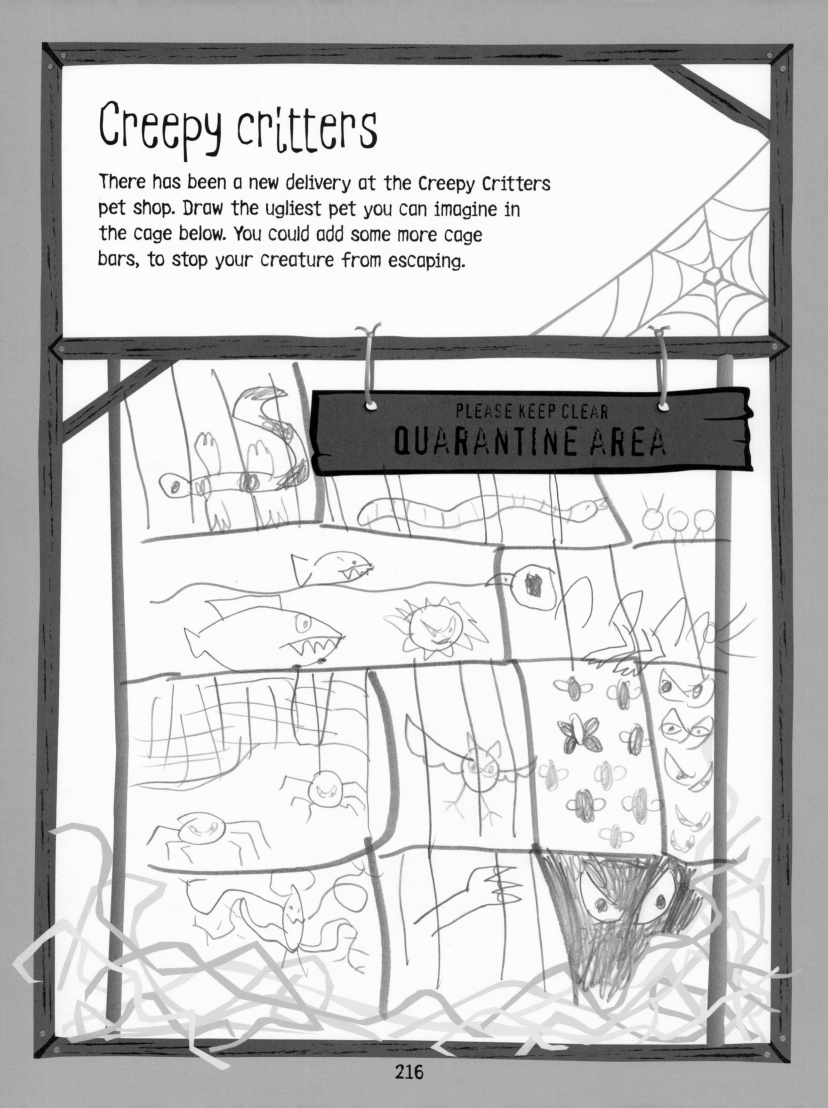

PLEASE KEEP CLEAR
QUARANTINE AREA

CREEPY CRITTERS

·SPECIALISTS IN DANGEROUS, DEVIOUS AND POISONOUS PETS·

Witches' cauldron

The broth is bubbling, ready for witches to weave a spooky spell. Draw some gruesome ingredients in the cauldron smoke.

Trick or treat?

Fill the Halloween bucket with sticky sweets and tempting treats.

Monster musical

It's showtime and the stage is set for the Spooks' Spectacular. Draw over the dotted lines and sketch your own talented terrors in the spotlights.

Gruesome garden

Use patterns and garish colors to make this garden as gruesome as you can. Zigzags, swirls, splats of goo and slime – use lots of colors and take your time!